G000161088

THE CHRISTMAS PARCEL

Noreen Walshe

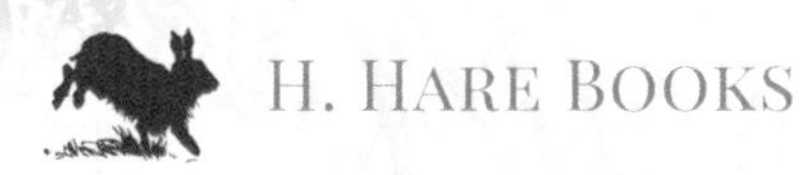
H. Hare Books

For Gerry Harte
The Keeper of Dreams
with Love

Copyright © Noreen Walshe, 2020
First Published in Ireland, in 2020, in co-operation with
Choice Publishing, Drogheda, County Louth, Republic of Ireland.
www.choicepublishing.ie
Typesetting & Layout (Paperback) by Tomas Korintus @ A & J Print Dunshaughlin Ltd.
Paperback ISBN: 978-1-913275-24-2
eBook ISBN: 978-1-913275-25-9
A CIP catalogue record for this book is available from the National Library.
All rights reserved. No part of this publication may be reproduced, stored in a retrieval system, transmitted in any form, or by any means, electronic, mechanical, photocopying, recording or otherwise, without the prior permission of the copyright holder.

Front Cover Painting - The Postman Calls
Back Cover Painting - Across at the Neighbours

Illustrations & Stories include:

King John Castle, Limerick iv
Cheeky Robin vi
In Flight viii
Mother Bear and Cub x

Bears on the Horizon **01**

The Postman Calls 02
Spruce Trees in the Tundra. 03
Mother Bear, Cub & Penguin 04
Reclining Bear 05
Inside the parcel 05
Mother Bear & Cub 06-07

The Tenth Carol **09**

Singing in the Kitchen 10
Knitting 11
The Christmas Story over Christy Mac's 12
Once in Royal David's City 13
Choir from Saint Patrick's Cathedral 14
The Robin

Christmas Star **17**

Lily Hickey's Shop on Lough Key. 18
The Best Ivy 19
Mr Butler's Horse and Trap 19
Clip-clopping towards the Gingerbread House 19
Christmas Baby 20
Mr Butler 21
In the Magic 21
Time to Take Dad Home 22
The Evening Star & the Crescent Moon 23

Across the Christmas Sky **25**

Across at the Neighbours 26
Christmas has come 27
Across the Christmas Sky 28
The Irregular Prayer Chain 29
My Cousin on her Scooter 30
The Spirits of the Dead 31
Time to stop Daydreaming 32
Tasting Snow 33

Ghosts **35**

At the Christmas Table - Times Past 36
One Man Production of 'A Christmas Carol' 37
The Wren Boys 38
A Happy Ghost at Christmas 39
My Christmas Table 40
The Pound Candle 41

"I truly believe that if we keep telling the Christmas story, singing the Christmas songs, and living the Christmas spirit, we can bring joy and happiness and peace to this world."

Norman Vincent Peale

Introduction

It was in front of a big log fire in the Auberge Otis, Baie St Paul in Québec, November 2008 that words and images began to arrange themselves like jigsaw pieces on a page.

I had just come down from the Northern area of Canada, Churchill on Hudson Bay, having visited the Tundra to see, photograph and draw Polar Bears. Churchill is after all the Polar Bear capital of the world and it certainly did not disappoint in its experience of the far north, snow, vegetation, wildlife and the presence of the great white giant of the Arctic.

I was alive on every level with newly collected material for paintings, stories touched by local mythology and the wonder of this place so removed from the everyday life of the Boyne Valley where I live and of course the Irish weather.

What charms my adult heart invariably touches into the world of my childhood and an interweaving of image, motif, word and story happens, drawing from many boxes within my mind. In this instance sentences became paragraph, paragraphs grew into narrative and so ensued the five distillations of the essence of Christmas for me as a child growing up on the Dublin Road in Limerick City in the 1950's.

Distillations are what I call them because of the intensity of recall, nostalgia and emotion that pours from each one of them like a single malt whiskey in the soft light of a Christmas evening. I loved writing these pieces. In a way they were balm for the soul. Self expression in response to moving and yet melancholic things that I had witnessed or experienced at an impressionable age.

Creating them invoked my parents, neighbours and friends long departed. I wonder sometimes if what we, the living, seem to be making into pieces of art are not projections of the dead onto paper and canvas through us. A lively exchange, a pooling of energies. A continuation of creativity beyond the veil....who knows?

I will be forever grateful to Maire Nic Gearailt, Broadcaster, Presenter and Producer of Lyric Notes, RTE LyricFM who accepted these scribblings for broadcast in the Quiet Quarter a section for New Irish Writing in her programme for the week before Christmas that year. She opened a window for me within the art of the written word and nurtured something deep within that needed expression through this medium. In the ‹The Quiet Quarter: Ten Years of Great Irish Writing› RTE LyricFM Published by New Island Books, 2009, the story 'Bears on the Horizon' was published and my painting ‹Fairy Tree - Tara› was used as a cover image. Again in 2015, Maire opened my Exhibition 'Spirit of Christmas Childhood in Limerick, a collection of illustrations for the same stories in the Hunt Museum, Limerick City. Now the text and images have become the book!

I feel blessed that my life is and has been graced with people, both living and deceased who have believed in me and through the power of their positive energy have brought me to this point where I can live and play in paint, print and magical ideas. The ultimate intention is to give back some beauty from the goodness of my own life.

Noreen Walshe © **2020**

Foreword

I met Noreen Walshe the writer before I met Noreen Walshe the artist.

I was presenting and producing Lyric Notes, the mid morning programme on RTÉ lyric fm and The Quiet Quarter was a segment within that, an outlet for new Irish writing.

I love music and was completely happy to be able to share that love on radio but got an equal satisfaction, maybe more so, from reading scripts submitted for broadcast in The Quiet Quarter.

There was a unique excitement and anticipation in opening an A4 envelope or an email attachment and seeing pages filled with words, with stories new, unknown, unread. That excitement and enthusiasm for a new set of scripts never waned. Some worked for radio, some didn't. Some were recorded and broadcast and some weren't.

Many I still remember reading for the first time and Noreen's were among those.

It was November 2008 and as I read through I realised that here was the Quiet Quarter for Christmas week. Noreen's childhood memories of Christmas came alive on the page, they were so powerful, so visual they sparkled and I have found rereading these stories now just as magical as I did the first time around.

I called Noreen to ask about recording them for broadcast over Christmas and it was then I learned that not only did she provide the writings but she could also supply the RTÉ Guide with the publicity they needed, her very own paintings to promote the Christmas Quiet Quarter - the complete package!

And that was when I met Noreen Walshe the Artist and I discovered she created Visual Magic as well. I went to have a look at some of her paintings on line and then she sent me a copy of "*Moving Carpet*", her stunning collection of her work as an artist from 1992 to 2001, a book to cherish, as any of you who has a copy knows and now we have its companion!

The following year I was compiling an anthology of 10 Years of The Quiet Quarter, being published by New Island Books, and there was only one place to turn to find an image for the cover so I gave Noreen a call and she presented me with the ideal illustration for the cover - her painting of the Fairy Tree - Tara.

All good things come to an end! And so did the programme Lyric Notes and the Quiet Quarter and I retired from RTÉ. I didn't expect the Quiet Quarter to raise its head again. However in late 2015 I got a call from Noreen to ask me if I would open an exhibition of her paintings in the Hunt Museum in Limerick. Then she told me that all the paintings were to be based on her radio pieces. I was absolutely thrilled, quite overcome, as I could never have foreseen that those pieces I enjoyed reading so much and listening to later when Noreen recorded them for transmission, would live on in captivating visual creations and eventually come together in this book. You have to make things happen and Noreen does!

On radio you make your own pictures but here we get to see the pictures as they exist for their creator.

There's the encounter with the polar bear in the Tundra of North Manitoba, that takes us spiralling backwards with Noreen to meet her four year old self, with the measles, receiving the parcel from her Auntie Tess in England that contained the tiny porcelain figure of the Mother Polar Bear and her Cub. We have The Tenth Carol where as Noreen sings she *"can see the whole Christmas story happening near Christy Mac's down the road. He has a farm and Dad says the same moon and stars that shone over Bethlehem are shining over our road."*

Christmas Eve when Noreen was five we get to meet Mr Butler with his Horse and Trap who invites her *"to see what we have in the stable"* .... the anticipation, the excitement! There's magic in the stable and love and wisdom in the eyes of the large dark cow, the new mother with her Christmas Baby**.** *"Born this morning, before you got out of bed."*

We can travel across the Christmas sky like a flying horse over Katie Crosse's house and return to simpler times when we were all young and everything we needed for Christmas was in the likes of Katie Crosses's window - we needed nothing more.

And then the Christmas Dinner Table where *"Invoked by my father's stories, long departed friends would saunter in, straight from the world of spirit and sit casually with us."*

Noreen has captured time and memory so vividly and perfectly, the wonder of it all, the magic, the ghosts, the spirit of her own childhood in Limerick.

I was honoured when Noreen asked me to open her exhibition in 2015 and even more so, five years later, to contribute to this enchanting collection.

Maire Nic Gearailt © 2020

Preface

Noreen Walshe's new work is as fine an evocation of a childhood Christmas as you are likely to find. It will stand beside my other favourites, *'A Child's Christmas in Wales'* by Dylan Thomas and Patrick Kavanagh's *'A Christmas Childhood'* next December to complete a trilogy. There is a rich nostalgia permeating the pages of this beautiful book, but there is more, much more than that.

If you have never met the author/artist, then this work is as good an introduction to Noreen as you could wish for. There are inspired and inspiring vignettes of prose accompanied by reproductions of her original paintings that together evoke a world of innocence and wonder; what Kavanagh describes as *"the gay garden that was childhood's..."* It is a book for the eternal child in all of us.

Appropriately the paintings were first exhibited in December 2015 in 'The Hunt Gallery' in Limerick, a gentle mile from Noreen's childhood home, and equally appropriately the stories were first broadcast from the Limerick studios of Lyric FM in 2008.

For though this book is about Christmas, it it also about Limerick, about a closely knit community on the Dublin Road, a small family and a little girl at the heart of it. Through her eyes a lost world is recovered for us to walk through, specifically during the Christmas of 1959, when she was, in the words of Kavanagh, *"six Christmases of age."* Her mother and father, *"beyond phone and spruce trees now, having travelled outside time and beyond the moon and stars"* are made to live again in word and picture.

The paintings reproduced in the book show us a world of fantasy where the little girl rides across the Christmas sky on a magical white horse while her parents, feet firmly on the earth, look on, watchful lest the magic should falter or fail. More precious than life itself, she is their only care.

The stories / memoirs written almost exclusively in the present tense allow us to time travel to the now of then and experience firsthand the warmth of a family, in their cosy little house, a veritable trinity of love. Times change. This book is for always...

Richard Ball © 2020

"I will honour Christmas in my heart, and try to keep it all the year.
I will live in the Past, the Present, and the Future. The Spirits of all Three shall strive within me.
I will not shut out the lessons that they teach."
Charles Dickens, (*A Christmas Carol*)

Acknowledgements

— My sincere thanks to the following people who have enabled my life to be better and more fulfilled as an artist, writer and human being.

— My husband Gerry Harte 'gets' me in my creativity, accommodates the Muse and cares for me in this incarnation with unconditional love.

— Máire Nic Gearailt, former presenter and editor of Lyric Notes, RTE LyricFM who opened an exciting window of possibility when she accepted my submission of five stories about Christmas as a child in Limerick in the 50's for broadcast in December 2008. Thank you for being with the soul project through radio, anthology, exhibition of illustrations and now the book.

— Richard and Mary Ball for their constant friendship and belief in the creative process. We share a rich tapestry of life colours and experiences.

— Pauline and Peter Murphy for their friendship, encouragement and constant support.

— Maedhbh Mac Namara and her husband Sean Byrne. Maedhbh has believed in me as an artist since we met on the bus en route to the Gaeltacht in 1970 as innocent teenagers. She has prodded, pushed and subtly pointed me in the direction of this book for a while now.

— Teresa O'Farrell for her wisdom and illumination over our years of friendship.

— Mary Woods - Friends forever, travelling companion and writing buddy.

— Jane Wardick, spiritual teacher and healer for her unique advice and insights that illuminate my journey.

— My family of cousins especially Eilish Foley with whom I grew up and shared dreams and stories of how families work.

— My neighbours near and far; those on the Dublin Road in Limerick and those who live close to me here in Meath.

— My friends from childhood; Geraldine Deegan, Mary Vaughan, Noreen and Betty Lawlor, John, Kay, Carol, Deirdre Flood and Mary Markham.

— John Byrne, Katherine McKenna, Kay Callan and Emer Walsh for wellness and energy building as a foundation for creativity.

— My 'tribe' of well-being, spiritual development and inquiry; Marion Finucane, Ruth Blessing, Niamh Scannell and Grace-Anne Kelly.

— John, Jackie McKeown and Grainne Rafter for support in difficult moments.

— Marie Hannon for her undying subtlety in pushing me and this book along.

— Gerardette Bailey, Arts Officer with Meath County Council. The book has happened at last, helped by the Professional Development Award granted to me in 2017!

— The Tyrone Guthrie Centre, Co. Monaghan for providing a most salubrious place in which to create and just 'be'.

— Deirdre Devine and her team at Choice Publishing for accepting to engage in their own creative way with this project.

— A & J Print for continued support and service over many years.

— Tomas Korintus for doing such honour to the content of this book, both text and image with his expertise in graphic design.

— There are those who have 're-emerged into the space of nonphysical consciousness' (Abraham Hicks) in particular Peggy McLellan who was always there to advise, encourage and to just say 'get on with it' through cups of tea and copious amounts of wisdom and empathy.

— Forever to my parents Tom and Mary who are constant companions to my daily life. They were and still are my genesis of creativity, inspiration and self-belief.

Bears on the Horizon

In the Tundra, in North Manitoba, outside of the town of Churchill, I saw my first live Polar Bear. This is where they say it takes two trees to make a Christmas tree due to the winter gales that burn the windward sides of the fragile spruce.

It's day three, early morning and we're already jolting along in a huge tundra buggy, scanning the horizon for the creamy white of even one bear. I'm in the company of a group of naturalists. While they search for the perfect photo, I dream of line, shape, pattern and colour, all the elements that will make an interesting painting.

There is a moment when we approach an oasis of aubergine-coloured willow bushes and we see the back of a prone white figure. The driver cuts the engine and tension fills the truck as cameras are lifted, focused and everyone is trying not to explode with excitement.

We're as close as is possible, to see the hairs of its coat and the coal black eyes slowly open. The round shape of a female's head rises above the bushes and watches us.

Winter is closing in as we wait in suspended animation to see what happens next.

With the first flurries of snow, a memory comes out of the arctic sky, gently at first, then tumbles down the stairs of so many years. It lands on the fourth step of my childhood and settles like the quiet world within a snow globe.

I'm standing behind my mother, inside the front door. She has a sprig of holly in her hand that has fallen off the Sacred Heart picture and I have the measles. As she opens the door, the snowflakes blow in onto the lino and the postman hands her a bulky, brown paper parcel tied with white twine. She puts her hand into her apron pocket and takes out a half crown, the Christmas Box. She hands it to him, they exchange greetings and he is gone.

My father said that Christmas began with his birthday on the twenty-sixth of November. My mother said it began on the eighth of December when the country people came to town to do their Christmas shopping.

Christmas began for me when the parcel came.

Every year, that parcel came from my auntie Tess in England and every year the Queen of England came with it, stamped in several images across the front and written in my aunt's handwriting on the side was 'Old clothing, personal belongings.'

There's a jumble of pictures in my head of the things that came over the years; hand-knitted socks, willow-pattern plates, a tiny jug with a hole in the bottom of it and jelly-babies. But this year it's different.

There's a jacquard waistcoat, a pipe with a packet of tobacco, a wraparound black coat 'for the opera' and a child's pea green jumper.

Stuffed into one of those green sleeves is a small package wrapped in a tissue. It's hard in the centre. I find three tiny figures hidden in there; a mother bear, her cub and a penguin, each standing on their own piece of ice, silent in an eternal winter of frozen porcelain.

I'm juggling the details of this memory when the gasps of excitement in present time call me back and I steady myself and my sketchbook and look out into the arctic desert.

My childhood memory has come alive. In front of my eyes, a small body, a cub's head appears above its mother's back. Mother looks to the left, turns, looks at us and leans over on the other side, deliberately and slowly moving four massive paws in the air.

Baby is missing for a minute but soon its head is seen nuzzling into its mother's belly. In a consorted effort of accommodation, the cub finds its milk, thrusts and pushes and then there's a visible relaxing of the smaller cream body. Mother with her left paw pulls her offspring closer and nurses it while sitting.

In that space between thoughts where dreams are born, I want to call my mother, talk to her and remind her of the parcel. I want to tell her about the real bears and the magic out here in this far off place with the pea-green sea but time has passed and many tides have washed the shores of Hudson Bay. She is beyond phones and spruce-trees now, having travelled outside of time and beyond the moon and stars. She lives in her own world, far from the Arctic Circle and the concerns of the ordinary day and night.

THE TENTH CAROL

I'm very young and I'm standing in the middle of the kitchen floor in Limerick. I've just started school and I have a song to sing. I'm giving my all to it. It's on page nineteen of my catechism and Dad knows it by heart.

'Come on,' he says, 'One more time.'

'Angels we have heard on high, sweetly singing o'er the plains.' We sing the chorus together 'Gloria in excelsis Deo'

Then we both laugh and I ask him why there are eggshells in the angel song and he laughs again. I don't ask him though, about the angels singing so high that they can be heard over the sound of airplanes. I just think about that.

As we finish singing, my mother looks up from her knitting and says,

'Is that one of the carols they sing on Christmas Eve, Tom? You know, in that programme, the Lesson of the Nine Carols? Oh, that reminds me', she continues. 'I must buy the sugar for the icing.'

My mother made two Christmas cakes every year and I would arrive home on foggy evenings to be met by seasonal smells coming from the kitchen. As an initiation into the queendom of culinary expertise, she would show me how to pierce the top of a rich fruitcake to see if it was cooked. She fluttered nervously with the birth of every dark cake, wondering if the fruit had sunk to the bottom and would my grandmother be disappointed. And then, she would lace it with brandy that would tickle my nostrils and make me sneeze.

She never iced our cake until the afternoon of Christmas Eve. This she did around the time of the carol service from Saint Patrick's cathedral in Dublin. The voices on the wireless guided her, as it were, through pasting on the icing and when the strains of the proud carol 'Once in Royal David's City' poured into the kitchen, she would work in a melody of white with the full-bodied voices of the choir.

Our house was too small for a Christmas tree. We had a pound candle and a crib that was put up on the kitchen press, the week before Christmas.

So here I am, singing with the plaster angels that are guarding the entrance to the crib. One of them is missing an arm and they're knee-high in snow-piles of cotton wool. Joseph, Mary, the shepherds and the three wise kings are all kneeling in adoration of the baby who hasn't arrived yet to the stable.

I'm wearing my tartan kilt and my socks are down around my ankles. The night is black outside and there's a draft coming in through the window.

As I sing, I can see the whole Christmas story happening near Christy Mac's down the road. He has a farm and Dad says the same moon and stars that shone over Bethlehem are shining over our road.

All the neighbours are out on the path, looking up in wonder at the heavens and just when the shepherds are about to hear the good news, my father says to my mother,

'Do you know Mary, 'Angels we have heard on high', I don't think that's one of those carols. I never heard that one on the wireless.'

He turns to me with a grin on his face, 'We'll call this the tenth carol, will we Noreen? We'll make it our own'.

He gets up from the fireside and he says 'let's show them.'

I don't know who THEY are but as he waves his hands and counts 'one, two, three.' I burst into song.

The two of us do an encore for my mother and the night, singing to the flames and the shadows, while keeping time to the rhythmic sounds of her knitting needles.

Christmas Star

JAC
IN TH
JUDY
A
B
C

Before the chatter of campus students, when the world was young on the banks of the Shannon and I was five years old, Christmas Eve was the most special day of the year.

With a heightened sense of urgency bordering on panic, my mother became a walking to-do list. My father and I went our own way, out the Dublin Road, across the Groody bridge and turned down Farrell's Road where the best ivy grew.

We spent the morning in Limerick, buying comics and herbs, sprouts and carrots and soap for my aunts.

A last look at the figures in Todds' windows and the toys in Lily Hickey's on Lough Quay and we were free. Hand in hand, we left my mother to the sounds of carols from Saint Patrick's cathedral and the rising steam of ham on the boil.

I see us both now, this particular Christmas Eve. There's my Dad, his lanky figure balanced on some moss covered broken down wall. He's reaching up, pulling stubborn tendrils of shiny dark ivy off a telegraph pole and I'm imagining them decorating the big white Christmas candle that he bought in Lily Hickey's shop.

I say

'Up there Daddy, there's better ones up there' and he reaches higher and higher and hands me the prizes. My knitted gloves are wringing wet and I'm pretending I'm smoking with the white breath that's coming out of my mouth into the cold air.

With my mind jumping from one thing to another, I suddenly hear a clip-clopping sound in the distance and as I turn around, I see Mr. Butler with his horse and trap.

He lives in the gingerbread house at the entrance to where the Blue Nuns live.

Smiling, he waves and greets us.

'Happy Christmas to you and yours, Tom' and my father says

'And many happy returns to you and your Missus'

By the time he catches up with his greeting and has pulled his horse to a halt, he beckons to me from the back of the trap.

'Come on' he says 'up with you there. I want you to see what we have in the stable'.

My father lifts me onto the step of the trap and as I am seating myself on the leather seat, Mr Butler adds

'I suppose you'll be needing hay for the reindeers tonight?'

I nod in silence and watch the chestnut backside of the horse shining like autumn conkers in the low sun as we are now clip-clopping the short distance to his house.

Seconds later, we are standing in the stable. It's dark except for a shaft of weak sun coming in through the half open window. There's warm breath rising from the corner. There's a stirring in the straw and from behind a large dark cow, four long legs stand up, unsteadily. From the mix of warmth and the sweet smell of dung, I can't get one word out of my mouth.

'Born this morning, before you got out of bed. A Christmas baby!' and Mr Butler laughs with my father.

They talk awhile, grown-ups' talk. I look at the dust dancing in the fading light and feel all warm inside with the magic that's in the stable.

A heavy frost is already in the air as we leave Mr. Butler and head for home, me carrying an armful of hay and Dad looking like the Christmas candle with ivy trailing out under his arm.

He's looking at the sky behind Limerick. It's orange and yellow. The evening star is just coming out and he says to me

'Isn't that a wonder now! Look over there behind Saint John's cathedral. There's the crescent moon appearing specially for Christmas... and there... do you see it? Venus, the Evening Star, is keeping it company'.

I look up at him and there are tears in his eyes. He's gone all soft so I take his big hand in mine and decide it's time to take him home.

Across the Christmas Sky

It's seven twenty in the morning. The neighbours' windows are lighting up across the way.

There are muffled sounds of excitement. Someone is laughing. There's a clatter of dishes as my father sets the table for breakfast.

The fire is blazing in the grate and Gormans' chimney is sending plumes of white smoke into the early morning sky. A delicious sense of happiness fills my shivering body. Christmas has come.

The stars are in their heaven and the moon is like a big flat plate of cream as families and old men form the irregular prayer chain down along the Dublin Road, under the railway bridge on the way to eight o'clock Mass.

'Happy Christmas' people call out and old men who never raise their voices in Summer, smile out loud and Dad's in his new overcoat and Mam is wearing her red toque hat.

We're going by Katie Crosse's house. It's all lit up. There's a white horse shining in the half moon window above the front door. He looks like he's ready to take off with his right leg pawing the air.

I start running sideways, clicking my heels to sound like a horse galloping; clip-clipipety clip, clip-clippety clop

I wonder what it would be like to be a flying horse above Katie Crosse's.

The wonder of it all, down below. The railway tracks and the bridge, Cunneen's yard with the tractor and all the houses on the Well Road. The cows in the sheds, their breath white in the dark morning.

And up there in the sky, a monk balances the moon on his head and the spirits of the dead are smiling. They live behind the clouds. There's stardust coming out of the chimneys and the sky is full of mystery and my cousin Eilish is flying by on her new scooter. I know what she got from Santa.

I wonder what I got. She waves and I wave back.

I'm up there too among the clouds now with the cold breeze whooshing by my face. I know one thing for sure though, God is up here, somewhere. Dad says he's everywhere. I'm looking for him when a falling star goes by and I know that that's a soul going to be born. I fell to Earth nearly seven years ago and I live with my parents across from Crosses' field on the way to Dublin.

I think you'd have to fly even higher above the clouds, to look for God.

I glance down over the Dublin Road. Dad is looking at his pocket watch again and I hear my mother say,

'Noreen, stop daydreaming. Father Kennedy will be on the altar and we'll be traipsing up the aisle with everyone looking at us'.

The first flakes of snow have started to fall from Heaven onto the Dublin Road. I don't know how, but, the white horse is back home in Katie Crosse's window. I'm walking between my parents. I stick my hands in my pockets and look up at the sky. I close my eyes and open my mouth.

The tattered white pieces of cloud that are now falling from the Christmas sky, land and melt like broken pieces of communion on my tongue.

Ghosts

We were never alone at the Christmas dinner table. There were my parents and me, accompanied by the ghosts of grandparents, aunts, renegade uncles and deviant cousins who all arrived, somewhere between the main course and the plum pudding.

Invoked by my father's stories, long departed friends would saunter in, straight from the world of spirit and sit casually with us. Oh yes, my Dad's emotions would come alive as he remembered and his eyes would fill up with tears and how those tears used to embarrass me when I was growing up.

Christmas day was indeed a day of ghosts and memories. While my mother and I tended to the practical details, my father could be heard saying things like,

'There it is, all over now for another year, all the rushing and fussing' or 'many a turkey is gone to its glory by now!' And he'd look at the sinking head in his glass of stout.

To build on the morose, he always finished Christmas day with an improvisation on 'A Christmas Carol' by Charles Dickens.

With Arthur Guinness as muse and my mother as silent witness to emotion and excess, my father, in a space that I venture to call 'transcendental', would absent himself from the dinner table. He would reappear from the shadows and would launch into a one-man production.

He acted his way through Scrooge, Bob Cratchitt, Tiny Tim and the Ghosts of Christmas Past, Present and Time to Come.

Once I remember him slipping outside the front door to bang on the knocker, much to the horror of my mother, who, let's say, was not given to dramatics of any sort, least of all in her husband. The ghost of Marley might well have fled in equal horror on seeing her face.

My own Christmas table has as many guests as memories and as the evening shadows fall after the dinner, I play through the ritual of remembering those who have left us and have come back, beckoned by a word or some other reminder.

A name, a glimpse inside some neighbour's window or simply the line of a long forgotten carol. I do not call them by name, for fear of seeming too caught up in the past. But, I suppose it's in my blood, this leaning towards the romantic and maybe the morose.

There comes a moment, late, every Christmas evening, when I hear my father say, in a voice of aged innocence;

'The wren boys will be here in the morning, at the crack of dawn', a pause and then, 'the sixth of January is only around the corner and we'll be seeing the cock-step in the evening.

The days will be getting longer and sure, we won't know ourselves 'til it's Easter again'. Silence and he continues 'do you know, Easter, I prefer it. A time of hope, new things' and silence again.

As mid-winter darkness once again engulfs our lengthening days, a Christmas card falls off the mantelpiece.

The candles burn low, spitting dying flames in defiance of the dark. I look around and in the shadows, I see my Dad, sprawled in his armchair, one hand loosely clutching the Christmas number of Ireland's Own. A faint but well intentioned snore is rising from his mouth.

Yes, Christmas Day is well and truly over, once again and my father has become a shadow of his former self. He's a happy ghost, with just a hint of a smile on his face.

Noreen Walshe

Noreen was born in Limerick and after an early career as a teacher, she went to study Painting in Dublin and Canada. She answers the call of two Muses; the one of painting and the other of writing. She lives with her husband Gerry, Timmy the dog and Sprite the cat in the heart of the Boyne Valley. All in all, a very interesting life with the best yet to come!

+ 353 86 394 6565 noreenwalshe@gmail.com
www.noreenwalshe.com noreenwalsheartist